BASTIEN PIANO BASICS
TECHNIC
LEVEL 1
BY JAMES BASTIEN

Contents

*To reinforce the feeling of achievement, the teacher or student may put a √ when the page has been mastered.

ISBN 0-8497-5281-7

2

C Major Position

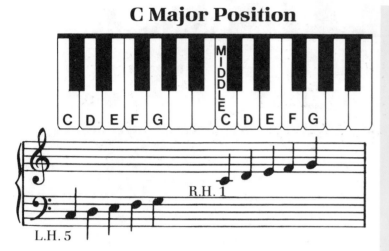

Practice Directions
1. Each exercise may be played hands separately at first.
2. Play evenly with curved fingers.
3. Play legato.
4. Play slowly at first; play faster when you are ready.
5. Use different dynamics; play loud (f) or soft (p).
Use these same practice directions for the rest of the book.

Warm-ups

*Continue this pattern up the keyboard on the white keys.

Stretching

*Continue this pattern up the keyboard on the white keys.

Skipping Stones

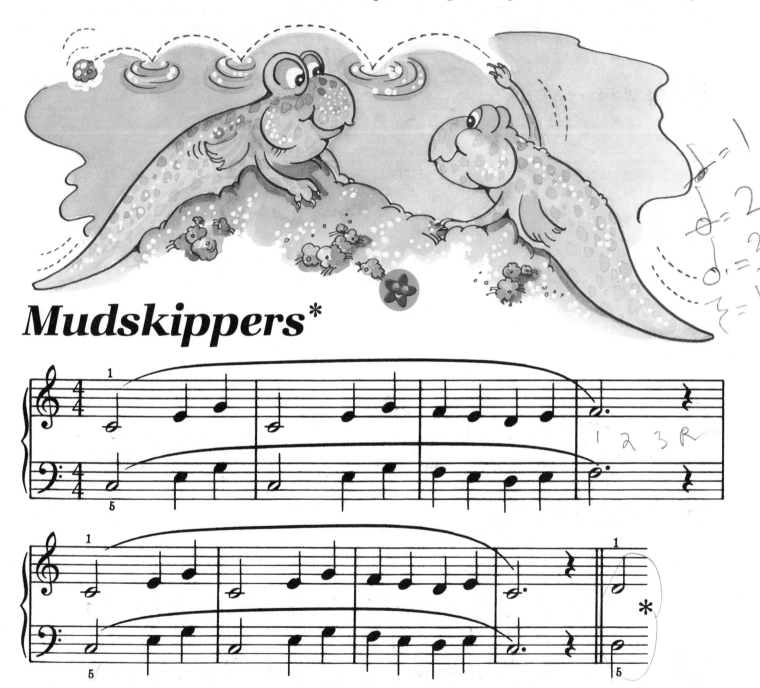

*Continue this pattern up the keyboard on the white keys.

Mudskippers*

*Continue this pattern up the keyboard on the white keys.

*Mudskippers are fish that can breathe in and out of water.

Use with page 7 of Piano, Level 1. **WP216**

Dolphins at Play

hands separately then together

Sharks!

I V⁷ Warm-up*

Play the L.H. softer than the R.H.

Keep Your Balance!

*Teacher: The interval of a 2nd represents the dominant harmony at this level. In Level 2, the three-note V7 chord is introduced and explained in detail.

Play the staccato notes short and separated.

Kangaroo Hops

Knock on Wood!

Play the staccato notes softer than the legato notes.

Pop, Pop!

Popcorn Popper

Jump and Slide

F Major Position

March of the Robots

Robot Race

Space Flight

Play the L.H. softer than the R.H.

Moon Walk

Use with pages 18-19 of Piano, *Level 1.* **WP216**

The Supertanker

Tugboat Tillie

Move your wrist from low to high in each slur.

Hang Gliding

Surfing

G Major Position

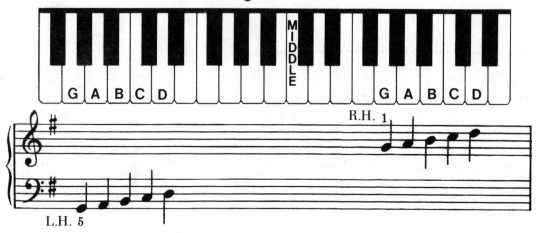

Gliding Intervals

Bouncing Intervals

WP216 *Use with pages 22-23 of Piano, Level 1.*

Funny Clowns

Clowning Around

G Major Position

Tricky Steps

The Basketball Game

Watch That Dribbling!

Let's Dance

Rockin' Rhythm

Tag! You're It!

Follow the Leader

Ocean Waves

Pedaling Along

Hop and Slide

Hop and Glide

The Bullfrog's Song

Leap Frog

Use with pages 36-37 of Piano, Level 1. **WP216**

Race to the Finish

Jumpin' Fun!

Use with pages 38-39 of Piano, Level 1.

Wind Surfing

Sailing Away

Play the L.H. softer than the R.H.

Angry Alligator

Mexican Fiesta

Lift Off!

Return to Earth

Exploring the Planets

Play these thirds smoothly.

A Pair of Parrots

Two by Two

Sledding We Go!

Special Requests for Technic